INTRODUCTORY Health Stories

Readings and Language Activities for Healthy Choices

Ann Gianola

Instructor, San Diego Community College District
Instructor, University of San Diego English Language Academy
San Diego, California

New Readers Press

Health Stories: Readings and Language Activities for Healthy Choices
Introductory Level
ISBN 978-1-56420-700-5

New Readers Press
ProLiteracy's Publishing Division
1320 Jamesville Avenue, Syracuse, New York 13210
www.newreaderspress.com

Printed in the United States of America
9 8 7 6 5 4

Proceeds from the sale of New Readers Press materials support professional
development, training, and technical assistance programs of ProLiteracy
that benefit local literacy programs in the U.S. and around the globe.

Developmental Editor: Paula L. Schlusberg
Creative Director: Andrea Woodbury
Illustrations: George Hamblin and Roger Audette, Represented by Wilkinson Studios Inc.
Production Specialist: Maryellen Casey

Contents

LESSON 1

Too Much Sodium

Jalal has high **blood** pressure.

It's a serious problem.

High **blood pressure** can cause a **heart attack.**

His doctor says, "Be careful about your **diet.**"

Sodium is not good for Jalal.

He can have only 1,500 **milligrams** every day.

Jalal wants some soup.

He reads a soup label at the store.

A cup of soup has 1,780 milligrams of sodium.

He can't eat that soup.

Jalal buys fresh foods and low-sodium soups.

Jalal tastes a new soup at home.
"It needs salt," says Jalal.
But Jalal pushes away the salt shaker.
He wants lower blood pressure.

Complete the story.

Jalal has _____ blood pressure. It's a serious problem.
                    1

High blood pressure can cause a _____ attack. His doctor
                                          2

says, "Be careful about your _____." Sodium is not good for
                                      3

Jalal. He can have only 1,500 milligrams every day.

Jalal wants some soup. He reads a soup _____ at the
                                                4

store. A cup of soup has 1,780 milligrams of _____.
                                                      5

He can't _____ that soup. Jalal buys fresh foods and
              6

low-sodium soups.

Jalal tastes a new soup at home. "It needs _____," says
                                                    7

Jalal. But Jalal pushes away the salt shaker. He wants _____
                                                                8

blood pressure.

Check *yes* or *no*.

Yes   No

___ ___   1. Jalal has low blood pressure.

___ ___   2. High blood pressure can cause a heart attack.

___ ___   3. His doctor says, "Be careful about your diet."

___ ___   4. Sodium is good for Jalal.

___ ___   5. Jalal reads a soup label at the doctor's office.

___ ___   6. A cup of soup has 1,780 milligrams of sodium.

___ ___   7. Jalal can eat the soup.

___ ___   8. Jalal buys fresh foods and low-sodium soups.

___ ___   9. Jalal puts salt on the new soup.

___ ___   10. Jalal wants lower blood pressure.

You decide.

Sodium is not good for Jalal. Check the foods that you think are good for him.

1. ___ potato chips

2. ___ broccoli

3. ___ pizza

4. ___ oranges

5. ___ carrots

6. ___ rice

7. ___ strawberries

8. ___ hot dogs

9. ___ cookies

10. ___ fresh fish

11. ___ low-sodium soups

12. ___ asparagus

At the Doctor's Office

Practice the dialog with a partner.

You have high blood pressure.
Oh, no. What can I do?
Be careful about your diet.
What can I eat?
Eat a lot of fresh foods.
Can I eat any canned foods?
Read labels for low-sodium items.

Nutrition Facts

Read the labels on the soup cans. Underline the correct answers.

Chicken Noodle Soup Nutrition Facts
Serving Size = 1/2 cup
Amount Per Serving   **Calories** 60
Total Fat 1.5g
Cholesterol 15mg
Sodium 890mg

Low-Sodium Vegetable Soup Nutrition Facts
Serving Size = 1/2 cup
Amount Per Serving   **Calories** 40
Total Fat 0g
Cholesterol 0mg
Sodium 215mg

1. One serving of chicken noodle soup has (**890 / 980**) milligrams of sodium.

2. I need to eat one (**calorie / cup**) to have 1,780 milligrams of sodium.

3. One serving of the low-sodium vegetable soup has (**215 / 20**) milligrams of sodium.

4. The (**low / high**) sodium soup is better for Jalal.

Understanding the Doctor

Listen to Jalal's doctor. Write the correct number next to each picture.

a. _____

d. _____

b. _____

e. _____

c. _____

Complete the sentences.

1. Jalal has _____.
   [a heart attack / high blood pressure]

2. _____ is not good for Jalal.
   [Sodium / His doctor]

3. _____ are good for Jalal.
   [Fresh foods / Salty foods]

4. Jalal wants _____.
   [a serious problem / lower blood pressure]

Think about it.

What can Jalal eat? Write your ideas on the lines.

_____   _____

_____   _____

Check yes or no about you.

Yes   No

____ ____   1. I watch my diet.

____ ____   2. I am careful with sodium.

____ ____   3. I buy fresh food.

____ ____   4. I want lower blood pressure.

LESSON 2

Pollen Problems

Eli doesn't like spring.

In April and May, there is tree **pollen** in the air.

Eli has an **allergy** to pollen.

"The trees are beautiful," says Eli's wife.

"Not to me," says Eli.

The windows in Eli's house are open.

A lot of tree pollen comes into the house.

Eli breathes in the tree pollen.

He **sneezes** a lot.

His eyes are **itchy** and watery.

Sometimes he gets a **headache.**

Eli closes the windows at home.
He wants to keep out the tree pollen.
In June, Eli opens the windows again.
"Close the windows, Eli," says
his wife.
"Summer is here. Grass pollen
is in the air."

Complete the story.

Eli doesn't like _____. In April and May, there is tree
_____ in the air. Eli has an _____ to pollen.
      2   3
"The trees are beautiful," says Eli's wife. "Not to me," says Eli.

The _____ in Eli's house are open. Tree pollen
      4
comes into the house. Eli _____ in the tree pollen. He
                               5
_____ a lot. His eyes are itchy and watery. Sometimes he
      6
gets a _____.
          7

Eli _____ the windows at home. He wants to keep out the
      8
tree pollen. In June, Eli opens the windows again. "Close the windows,
Eli," says his wife. "_____ is here. Grass pollen is in the air."
          9

Check *yes* or *no*.

Yes   No

____ ____   1. Eli likes spring.

____ ____   2. There is tree pollen in the air.

____ ____   3. Eli's wife says the trees are beautiful.

____ ____   4. His wife has an allergy.

____ ____   5. Eli's eyes are itchy and watery.

____ ____   6. He coughs a lot.

____ ____   7. Eli closes windows at home.

____ ____   8. He wants to keep in the tree pollen.

____ ____   9. In July, he opens the windows again.

____ ____ 10. In summer, grass pollen is in the air.

Allergies

Match the words and pictures.

| medication | pets | perfume |

1. _____   2. _____   3. _____

Talking with a Doctor

Practice the dialog with a partner.

I am allergic to pollen.

What are your symptoms?

My eyes are itchy and watery.

I sneeze a lot too.

Sometimes I get a headache.

Try some allergy medicine.

Do I need a prescription?

**First take something
over-the-counter.**

Symptoms

Eli is allergic to pollen. Check Eli's symptoms.

1. ____ runny nose

2. ____ watery eyes

3. ____ feeling tired

4. ____ sneezing

5. ____ itchy throat

6. ____ sore throat

7. ____ cough

8. ____ headache

9. ____ itchy eyes

10. ____ red eyes

Understanding the Doctor

Listen to Eli's doctor. Write the correct number next to each picture.

a. _____

d. _____

b. _____

e. _____

c. _____

f. _____

Complete the sentences.

1. Eli doesn't like _____.
   [spring / his wife]

2. Eli has _____.
   [a tree / an allergy]

3. His eyes are _____.
   [beautiful / itchy and watery]

4. Eli closes _____ at home.
   [the windows / his eyes]

Think about it.

What can help Eli feel better? Write your ideas on the lines.

_____   _____

_____   _____

Check *yes* or *no* about you.

Yes   No

____ ____   1. I like spring.

____ ____   2. I have an allergy.

____ ____   3. My eyes are itchy and watery.

____ ____   4. I sneeze a lot.

LESSON 3

Tired at Work

Tina likes late-night TV.
Her favorite shows begin at 11:30 P.M.
Sometimes she watches TV until 1:30 A.M.

Tina is **tired** in the morning.
Sometimes she falls asleep at work.
A co-worker taps her on the **shoulder.**
"Wake up, Tina!" she says.
Tina opens her eyes.
"Do you want to get fired?" asks
the co-worker.
"You need more sleep!"

Tina puts her head down on the desk again.
She closes her eyes.
"Let me sleep five more minutes,"
answers Tina.
"I can't miss my favorite shows tonight."

Complete the story.

Tina likes late-night TV. Her favorite _____ begin at
₁
11:30 P.M. Sometimes she _____ TV until 1:30 A.M.
₂

Tina is _____ in the morning. Sometimes she falls asleep at
₃
work. A _____ taps her on the shoulder. "Wake up, Tina!"
₄
she says. Tina opens her eyes. "Do you want to get _____?"
₅
asks the co-worker. "You need more _____!"
₆

Tina puts her _____ down on the desk again. She closes
₇
her eyes. "Let me sleep five more minutes," answers Tina. "I can't miss
my _____ shows tonight."
₈

Check *yes* or *no*.

Yes No

____ ____ 1. Tina likes late-night TV.

____ ____ 2. Her favorite shows begin at 1:30 A.M.

____ ____ 3. Tina is tired in the morning.

____ ____ 4. Sometimes she watches TV at work.

____ ____ 5. A co-worker taps her on the eyes.

____ ____ 6. A co-worker says, "Wake up, Tina!"

____ ____ 7. Tina wants to get fired.

____ ____ 8. Tina needs more sleep.

____ ____ 9. She puts her head down on the desk again.

____ ____ 10. Tina wants to sleep fifteen more minutes.

You decide.

Check the things Tina needs to do.

1. ____ work

2. ____ watch TV

3. ____ visit friends

4. ____ eat

5. ____ talk on the phone

6. ____ shop for clothes

7. ____ go to school

8. ____ exercise

9. ____ go to a hair salon

10. ____ sleep

11. ____ do laundry

12. ____ go to movies

Talking with a Co-worker

Practice the dialog with a partner.

Wake up!

Oh, sorry. I'm really tired today.

Why are you so tired?

I like late-night TV.

Do you want to get fired?

Of course I don't.

Then turn off the TV. You need more sleep.

Employee Handbook

Read the work rules. Answer the questions.

You may be **immediately dismissed** for:
- use of drugs or alcohol
- harassment
- theft
- sleeping on the job
- dishonesty
- repeated absences or lateness

1. What's another word for *fired* in the handbook? _____

2. Which rule does Tina break? _____

Check the correct picture.

1.

   a. _____   b. _____

3.

   a. _____   b. _____

2.

   a. _____   b. _____

4.

   a. _____   b. _____

Speaking Up

A co-worker is sleeping at her desk. What can I say? Check the good ideas.

_____ Good morning.

_____ You need more sleep.

_____ Would you like some coffee?

_____ You're fired.

_____ Do you need a pillow?

_____ You can sleep five more minutes.

_____ Wake up.

_____ I'm tired too.

_____ Do you want to get fired?

_____ You can't do that here.

_____ Sweet dreams.

_____ The boss can see you.

Complete the sentences.

1. Tina likes _____.
   [the morning / late-night TV]

2. Sometimes she _____ at work.
   [falls asleep / watches TV]

3. A co-worker taps her on the _____.
   [shoulder / head]

4. Tina needs more _____.
   [TV shows / sleep]

Think about it.

What can help Tina get more sleep? Write your ideas on the lines.

_____   _____

_____   _____

Check *yes* or *no* about you.

Yes   No

____ ____   1. I like late-night TV.

____ ____   2. I fall asleep at work.

____ ____   3. I need more sleep.

____ ____   4. I want to get fired.

LESSON 4

A Painting Accident

Koji is a house painter.
He is painting Mrs. Cole's house yellow.
Koji is up high on a ladder.

Koji loses his **balance.**
He falls off the ladder.
He **hurts** his leg very badly.
Mrs. Cole calls an **ambulance.**

Koji goes to the hospital.
He has an **x-ray.** His leg is **broken.**
The doctor sets the **bone.**

Koji is at home.
He can't work for six weeks.
The telephone rings. It is Mrs. Cole.
"Sorry I can't paint your house yellow,"
says Koji.
"That's okay," says Mrs. Cole. "Now
I want it blue."

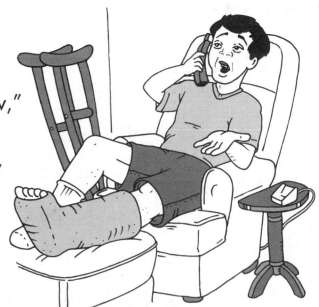

Complete the story.

Koji is a house painter. He is painting Mrs. Cole's _____

yellow. Koji is up high on a _____.

2

Koji loses his _____. He falls off the ladder. He hurts his

3

_____ very badly. Mrs. Cole calls an _____.

4   5

Koji goes to the hospital. He has an _____. His leg is

6

broken. The doctor sets the _____.

7

Koji is at home. He can't work for six weeks. The telephone rings.

It is Mrs. Cole. "Sorry I can't _____ your house yellow,"

8

says Koji.

"That's okay," says Mrs. Cole. "Now I want it blue."

Check *yes* or *no*.

Yes   No

____ ____ 1. Koji is a doctor.

____ ____ 2. He is painting Mrs. Cole's house yellow.

____ ____ 3. Koji is up high on a ladder.

____ ____ 4. Koji loses his paintbrush.

____ ____ 5. He falls off the ladder.

____ ____ 6. Mrs. Cole calls another painter.

____ ____ 7. Koji has an x-ray.

____ ____ 8. He has a broken arm.

____ ____ 9. The doctor sets the bone.

____ ____ 10. Koji can't work for six months.

You decide.

Check the things you think Koji needs.

1. ____ crutches

2. ____ doctor

3. ____ ladder

4. ____ x-ray

5. ____ money

6. ____ hospital

7. ____ pain medication

8. ____ yellow paint

9. ____ physical therapy

10. ____ new job

11. ____ ambulance

12. ____ cast

Talking to a Paramedic

Practice the dialog with a partner.

Help me, please!

What happened?

I fell off a ladder.

Where does it hurt?

It's my leg. I think it's broken.

Don't move. We'll get you to the hospital.

Ladder Safety

Circle the right way to stand on a ladder.

a.

b.

Doctor's Orders

Listen to Koji's doctor. Write the correct number next to each picture.

a. ____

d. ____

b. ____

e. ____

c. ____

f. ____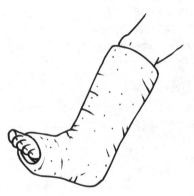

Complete the sentences.

1. Koji is painting Mrs. Cole's _____.
   [house / hospital]

2. He loses his _____.
   [telephone / balance]

3. Mrs. Cole calls _____.
   [a doctor / an ambulance]

4. His _____ is broken.
   [leg / ladder]

Think about it.

What can help Koji feel better? Write your ideas on the lines.

_____   _____

_____   _____

Check *yes* or *no* about you.

Yes   No

____ ____   1. I sometimes use a ladder.

____ ____   2. I have a broken leg.

____ ____   3. I can call for an ambulance.

____ ____   4. I can work.

LESSON 5

More Exercise

Fran and Bill need more **exercise.**
They have no **energy.**
They sit at home. They sit at work.
They sit in the car.

Fran sees a flyer for an exercise class.
It is at the recreation center.
It is only four blocks from home.
"Let's go," says Fran.
"Good idea," says Bill.

Fran and Bill put on their exercise clothes.

Fran picks up a bottle of water.

Bill picks up the car keys.

"We can walk," says Fran.

"I don't want to get too tired," says Bill.

"Let's drive."

Complete the story.

Fran and Bill need more _____. They have no

_____. They sit at home. They sit at work. They
_____2_____

_____ in the car.
_____3_____

Fran sees a flyer for an exercise _____. It is at the
_____4_____

recreation center. It is only four _____ from home. "Let's
_____5_____

go," says Fran.

"Good idea," says Bill.

Fran and Bill put on their exercise clothes. Fran picks up a bottle of

_____. Bill picks up the _____ keys. "We can
_____6_____   _____7_____

walk," says Fran.

"I don't want to get too _____," says Bill. "Let's drive."
_____8_____

Check *yes* or *no*.

Yes   No

____ ____ 1. Fran and Bill need more exercise.

____ ____ 2. They have a lot of energy.

____ ____ 3. They sit at home, at work, and in the car.

____ ____ 4. Fran sees a flyer for an exercise class.

____ ____ 5. It is only four miles from home.

____ ____ 6. Fran and Bill put on their driving clothes.

____ ____ 7. Fran picks up a bottle of water.

____ ____ 8. Bill picks up the recreation center keys.

____ ____ 9. Fran says, "Let's drive."

____ ____ 10. Bill doesn't want to get too tired.

You decide.

Why do Fran and Bill need exercise? Check the things exercise can help.

1. ____ bones

2. ____ car keys

3. ____ heart

4. ____ weight

5. ____ water

6. ____ stress

7. ____ energy

8. ____ lungs

9. ____ appearance

10. ____ disease

11. ____ sofa

12. ____ muscles

Talking to a Doctor

Practice the dialog with a partner.

I have no energy.

Well, you're about 40 pounds overweight.

I know. I sit all the time.

You need to be more active.

What can I do?

Try walking. It's great exercise.

Calories

Read the things Fran and Bill do. Look at the number of calories they can burn in one hour.

Underline the correct answers.

	Fran	Bill
Watching TV	102	132
Driving	204	264
Walking	337	436
Doing Aerobics	510	660
Sitting at Work	153	198

1. Fran burns (**102 / 132**) calories watching TV.

2. Bill burns (**204 / 264**) calories driving.

3. Fran burns 153 calories (**sitting at work / driving**).

4. Bill burns 436 calories (**walking / doing aerobics**).

What Fran Does

Listen to Fran's activities. Write the correct number next to each picture.

a. _____

d. _____

b. _____

e. _____

c. _____

f. _____

Complete the sentences.

1. Fran and Bill have no _____.
   [home / energy]

2. Fran sees a flyer for an exercise _____.
   [class / clothes]

3. The recreation center is only four blocks from _____.
   [their car / home]

4. Bill wants to drive. He doesn't want to get too _____.
   [thirsty / tired]

Think about it.

What can help Fran and Bill feel better? Write your ideas on the lines.

_____   _____

_____   _____

Check *yes* or *no* about you.

Yes   No

____ ____   1. I need more exercise.

____ ____   2. I sit a lot.

____ ____   3. I go to exercise class.

____ ____   4. I walk when I can.

LESSON 6

No More Candy

Bella has a seven-year-old son.
His name is Gino.
Gino eats a lot of candy.
He forgets to brush his teeth.
Gino's teeth hurt.

Bella takes Gino to the **dentist.**
The dentist **examines** him.
She **x-rays** his teeth.
Gino has six **cavities.**
"No more candy," says the dentist.
"Brush your teeth twice a day."

No more candy!

Bella makes another **appointment.**
Gino needs to come back for **fillings.**
The dentist gives Gino a toothbrush.
"Thank you," says Gino.
"Can I also have a lollipop?"

Complete the story.

Bella has a seven-year-old son. His name is Gino. Gino eats a lot of

_____. He forgets to _____ his teeth. Gino's

     1   2

_____ hurt.

     3

Bella takes Gino to the _____. The dentist examines him.

                                 4

She x-rays his teeth. Gino has six _____. "No more candy,"

                                 5

says the dentist. "Brush your teeth _____ a day."

                                 6

Bella makes another appointment. Gino needs to come back for

_____. The dentist gives Gino a _____.

     7   8

"Thank you," says Gino. "Can I also have a lollipop?"

Check *yes* or *no*.

Yes   No

____ ____ 1. Bella has a six-year-old son.

____ ____ 2. Bella eats a lot of candy.

____ ____ 3. Gino forgets to brush his teeth.

____ ____ 4. Bella takes Gino to the dentist.

____ ____ 5. She x-rays his stomach.

____ ____ 6. Gino has six cavities.

____ ____ 7. He needs to brush his teeth twice a day.

____ ____ 8. Bella makes another appointment.

____ ____ 9. Gino needs to come back for six lollipops.

____ ____ 10. The dentist gives Gino a toothbrush.

Take care of your teeth.

Match the words and pictures.

dentist	x-ray	toothpaste/toothbrush

1. _____

2. _____

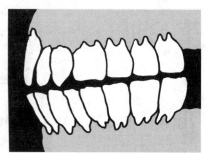

3. _____

Talking to the Dentist

Practice the dialog with a partner.

Your son has six cavities.

That isn't good news.

He needs to stop eating so much candy.

What else can I do?

Make sure he brushes twice a day.

What kind of toothpaste?

Use one with fluoride.

Toothpaste

Read the toothpaste label. Underline the correct answers.

> # Smile Fresh
> ## Toothpaste
> **Active ingredient** Sodium fluoride 0.24%
>
> **Use** Helps protect against cavities
>
> **Directions** Adults and children: brush teeth after meals or at least twice a day, or use as directed by a dentist

1. The active ingredient is sodium (**fluoride** / **fillings**).

2. This toothpaste protects against (**candy** / **cavities**).

3. Adults and children need to brush (**before** / **after**) meals.

4. Gino needs to brush at least (**once** / **twice**) a day.

At the Dentist

Listen. Write the correct number next to each picture.

a. ____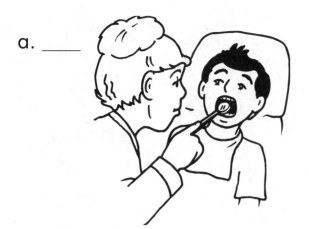

d. ____

b. ____

e. ____

c. ____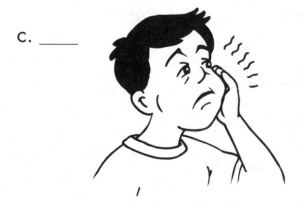

Complete the sentences.

1. Gino eats a lot of _____.
   [toothpaste / candy]

2. Gino forgets to _____ his teeth.
   [brush / x-ray]

3. His _____ hurt.
   [teeth / fillings]

4. The dentist gives him a _____.
   [lollipop / toothbrush]

Think about it.

What can help Gino's teeth feel better? Write your ideas on the lines.

_____   _____

_____   _____

Check *yes* or *no* about you.

Yes   No

____ ____   1. I eat a lot of candy.

____ ____   2. I brush my teeth.

____ ____   3. I go to the dentist.

____ ____   4. I have fillings.

LESSON 7

Wash Your Hands

Luís is a cook in a restaurant.
Diego is a new worker.
Diego walks into the kitchen.
"**Wash** your hands," says Luís.

Diego is busy all day.
He prepares food.
He empties the garbage.
He mops the floor.
He cleans the restroom.
After every job, Luís tells Diego
to wash his hands.

Diego finishes work at 10:00 P.M.
"Thanks for your help," says Luís.
Then Luís hands Diego a $10 tip.
"Money is very dirty," says Diego.
"Don't forget to wash your hands."

Complete the story.

Luís is a cook in a _____. Diego is a new worker. Diego
                          1
walks into the kitchen. "Wash your _____," says Luís.
                                            2

Diego is busy all day. He prepares _____. He empties
                                            3
the garbage. He mops the _____. He cleans the
                                  4
_____. After every job, Luís tells Diego to _____
        5   6
his hands.

Diego finishes work at 10:00 P.M. "Thanks for your

_____," says Luís. Then Luís hands Diego a $10 tip.
        7

"Money is very _____," says Diego. "Don't forget to wash
                      8
your hands."

Check *yes* or *no*.

Yes   No

____ ____ 1. Luís is a cook in a restaurant.

____ ____ 2. Diego is a new worker.

____ ____ 3. Diego doesn't wash his hands all day.

____ ____ 4. Diego prepares food.

____ ____ 5. Diego mops the garbage.

____ ____ 6. After every job, Luís hands Diego $10.

____ ____ 7. Diego finishes work at 11:00.

____ ____ 8. Luís says, "Thanks for the help."

____ ____ 9. Luís hands Diego a $10 tip.

____ ____ 10. Luís says, "Money is very dirty."

You decide.

You need to wash your hands after you touch some things. Check those things.

1. ____ food

2. ____ soap

3. ____ money

4. ____ cleaning supplies

5. ____ water

6. ____ raw meat

7. ____ chemicals

8. ____ things in a restroom

9. ____ garbage

10. ____ open cuts

11. ____ cigarettes

12. ____ mouths and noses

Talking to a New Worker

Practice the dialog with a partner.

Are you busy?

Yes. I'm cleaning the restroom.

Can you help me when you're done?

Sure. What do you need?

I need help with the salad.

I can do it in five minutes.

Thanks. Don't forget to wash
your hands.

Washing Your Hands

Read the hand-washing poster.

- Use soap and warm running water.
- Rub your hands for 15 seconds.
- Wash wrists and backs of hands.
- Wash between fingers and under fingernails.
- Rinse well.
- Dry hands with a paper towel.
- Turn off water with a paper towel.

Wash your hands!

Listen to the hand-washing steps. Write the correct number next to each picture.

a. ____

d. ____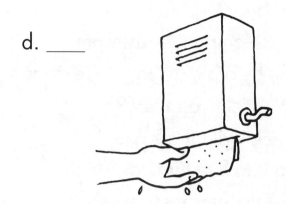

b. ____

e. ____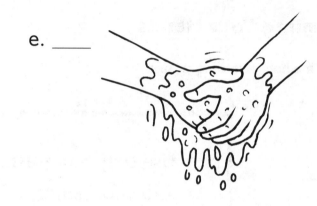

c. ____

f. ____

Complete the sentences.

1. Diego is a new _____.
   [worker / cook]

2. After every job, Diego _____ his hands.
   [waters / washes]

3. He rubs his hands for 15 _____.
   [salads / seconds]

4. He dries his hands with a paper _____.
   [towel / tip]

Think about it.

When do you wash your hands? Write the times on the lines.

_____   _____

_____   _____

Check *yes* or *no* about you.

Yes   No

____ ____   1. I prepare food.

____ ____   2. I empty garbage.

____ ____   3. I mop floors and clean restrooms.

____ ____   4. I always wash my hands.

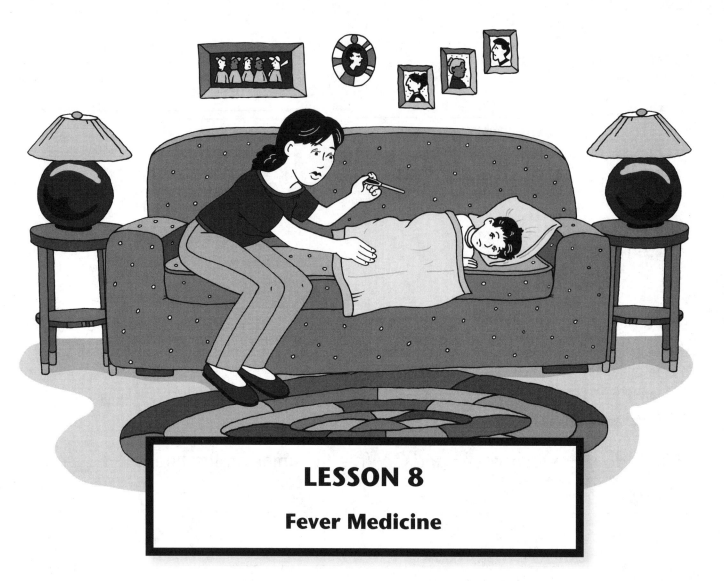

LESSON 8

Fever Medicine

Maria's son is José. He is two years old.
José doesn't feel well.
Maria takes his **temperature.**
It's 101 degrees. José has a **fever.**

Maria opens the **medicine cabinet.**
She finds some child fever medicine.
She looks at the date on the label.
This medicine is too old.
This medicine is **expired.**
She can't use it.

Maria goes to the **pharmacy.**
She picks up new medicine
for José.
Now Maria doesn't feel well.
Her **forehead** feels hot.
Maybe she has José's **virus.**
Maria buys some adult fever
medicine too.

Complete the story.

Maria's _____ is José. He is two years old. José doesn't
₁

feel well. Maria takes his _____. It's 101 degrees. José has
₂

a _____.
₃

Maria opens the medicine cabinet. She finds some child fever

_____. She looks at the _____ on the label. This
₄ ₅

medicine is too old. This medicine is _____. She can't use it.
₆

Maria goes to the _____. She picks up new medicine for
₇

José. Now Maria doesn't feel well. Her forehead feels hot. Maybe she

has José's virus. Maria buys some _____ fever medicine too.
₈

Check *yes* or *no*.

Yes   No

____ ____   1. Maria's son is one year old.

____ ____   2. José doesn't feel well.

____ ____   3. Maria takes José's temperature.

____ ____   4. It's 102 degrees.

____ ____   5. José has an earache.

____ ____   6. Maria finds some child fever medicine.

____ ____   7. The medicine is expired.

____ ____   8. Maria goes to the pharmacy.

____ ____   9. She picks up more expired medicine.

____ ____   10. Maria buys some adult fever medicine too.

You decide.

How can Maria help José? Check the things she can use.

1. ____ thermometer

2. ____ pharmacy

3. ____ toothbrush

4. ____ fluids

5. ____ doctor

6. ____ Internet

7. ____ child fever medicine

8. ____ hand lotion

9. ____ children's health book

10. ____ antibiotics

11. ____ soup

12. ____ adult fever medicine

At the Pharmacy

Practice the dialog with a partner.

My two-year-old has a fever.
What can he take?
He can take these drops.
How do I give them to him?
Use the dropper inside the bottle.
Thank you.

Taking Medicine

Read the label on the fever medicine. Look at the dropper. Answer the questions.

Weight (lb.)	Age (yr.)	Dose
Under 24	Under 2	Call a doctor
24-35	2-3	1.6 mL (0.8 + 0.8 mL)
If needed, repeat dose every four hours.		
EXP. DATE: 04/08		

1. How much medicine does José need? _____

2. How many times does Maria need to fill the dropper? _____

3. When does this medicine expire? _____

4. It's 2:00. What time can José take this medicine again? _____

Check the correct picture.

1.

   a. ____   b. ____

3.

   a. ____   b. ____

2.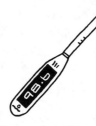

   a. ____   b. ____

4.

   a. ____   b. ____

Complete the sentences.

Use *child* or *adult* in each sentence.

1. José is two years old. He needs _____ fever medicine.

2. Maria is 30 years old. She needs _____ fever medicine.

3. I am 20 years old. I need _____ fever medicine.

4. You are 16 years old. You need _____ fever medicine.

5. She is three years old. She needs _____ fever medicine.

6. He is 40 years old. He needs _____ fever medicine.

Complete the sentences.

1. José doesn't feel well. His temperature is 101 _____.
[fever / degrees]

2. Maria opens the _____.
[pharmacy / medicine cabinet]

3. She looks at the _____ on the label.
[date / temperature]

4. This medicine is _____. She can't use it.
[hot / expired]

Think about it.

What can help José feel better? Write your ideas on the lines.

_____   _____

_____   _____

Check *yes* or *no* about you.

Yes   No

____ ____   1. I take medicine when I have a fever.

____ ____   2. I look at the date on medicine labels.

____ ____   3. I use expired medicine.

____ ____   4. I have child and adult fever medicine at home.

LESSON 9

Calling 911

Ming and Dora are neighbors.
Ming sees Dora in the laundry room.
Dora is holding her **chest.**
"I don't feel well," says Dora.
"My chest hurts."

Ming tells Dora not to worry.
She calls 911 on her cell phone.
"My neighbor is having chest pains," says Ming.
Ming gives the address of the apartment building.
The **paramedics** arrive in ten minutes.

The paramedics examine Dora.
They give her some **oxygen.**
"How old is she?" asks a paramedic.
"I think she's about 75," says Ming.
Dora takes off the oxygen mask.
"Thank you," she says. "I'm really 81."

Complete the story.

Ming and Dora are _____. Ming sees Dora in the laundry
<u>1</u>

room. Dora is holding her _____. "I don't feel well," says
<u>2</u>

Dora. "My chest hurts."

Ming tells Dora not to _____. She calls 911 on her cell
<u>3</u>

phone. "My neighbor is having chest _____," says Ming.
<u>4</u>

Ming gives the address of the apartment building. The paramedics

arrive in ten minutes.

The _____ examine Dora. They give her some
<u>5</u>

_____. "How _____ is she?" asks a paramedic.
<u>6</u>   <u>7</u>

"I think she's about 75," says Ming. Dora takes off the oxygen

_____.
<u>8</u>

"Thank you," she says. "I'm really 81."

Check *yes* or *no*.

Yes   No

____ ____ 1. Ming and Dora are paramedics.

____ ____ 2. Ming sees Dora in the laundry room.

____ ____ 3. Dora is holding her chest.

____ ____ 4. Ming tells Dora to worry.

____ ____ 5. Ming calls 911 on her cell phone.

____ ____ 6. The paramedics arrive in 75 minutes.

____ ____ 7. The paramedics examine Ming.

____ ____ 8. The paramedics give Dora some oxygen.

____ ____ 9. A paramedic asks how old Dora is.

____ ____ 10. Dora is really 81.

You decide.

Someone is having chest pains. What can help them?

1. ____ paramedics

2. ____ oxygen

3. ____ food

4. ____ 911

5. ____ laundry

6. ____ hospital

7. ____ ambulance

8. ____ water

9. ____ medicine

10. ____ doctor

11. ____ neighbor

12. ____ cell phone

Talking to a 911 Operator

Practice the dialog with a partner.

What is the emergency?

My neighbor is having chest pains.

Where are you?

We're at the Parkview Apartments.

What is the address?

It's 5290 G Street.

What's your name?

My name is Ming Chen.

Dora's Purse

Look at the things in Dora's purse. Write the number for each item on the line.

Circle the things the paramedics and Ming can use to help Dora.

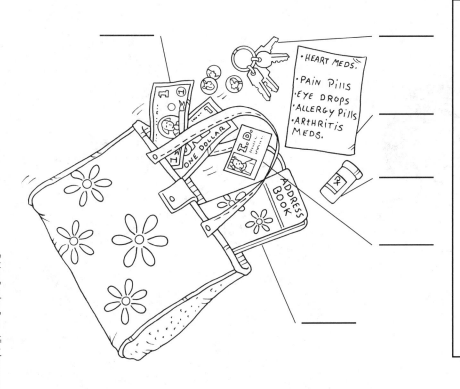

1. address book

2. identification

3. keys

4. list of medications

5. medication

6. money

Emergency

Listen to the events. Write the correct number next to each picture.

a. ____

d. ____

b. ____

e. ____

c. ____

f. ____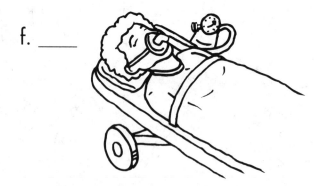

Complete the sentences.

1. Dora is holding her _____.
   [chest / purse]

2. She says, "I don't feel _____."
   [worry / well]

3. Ming calls _____ on her cell phone.
   [911 / 81]

4. The paramedics give Dora some _____.
   [medication / oxygen]

Think about it.

What can help Dora? Write your ideas on the lines.

_____   _____

_____   _____

Check *yes* or *no* about you.

Yes   No

___   ___   1. I know my neighbor's name.

___   ___   2. I know how old my neighbor is.

___   ___   3. I can help someone with chest pains.

___   ___   4. I can call 911.

LESSON 10

Visiting Hours

Elsa's friend is in the **hospital.**
Elsa wants to visit her.
She sees a sign on the wall.
Visiting Hours: 10:00 A.M. to 8:30 P.M.
It is 8:00 P.M. now.

Elsa waits at the **reception desk.**
She finds out her friend is in Room 579.
Elsa waits for the elevator.
The elevator doesn't open.
Then she sees another sign: *Out of Order.*

Elsa takes the stairs to the fifth floor.

There are many rooms.

Finally she sees Room 579.

"Sorry," says the **nurse.**

"Visiting hours are over.

You can come back tomorrow at 10:00 A.M."

Complete the story.

Elsa's friend is in the _____. Elsa wants to visit her. She

_____ 1

sees a _____ on the wall. Visiting _____:

_____ 2 _____ 3

10:00 A.M. to 8:30 P.M. It is 8:00 P.M. now.

Elsa waits at the _____ desk. She finds out her friend is in

_____ 4

Room 579. Elsa _____ for the elevator. The elevator doesn't

_____ 5

open. Then she sees another sign: _____ of Order.

_____ 6

Elsa takes the _____ to the fifth floor. There are many

_____ 7

rooms. Finally she sees Room 579. "Sorry," says the _____.

_____ 8

"Visiting hours are over. You can come back tomorrow at 10:00 A.M."

Check *yes* or *no*.

Yes   No

____ ____ 1. Elsa's friend is in the hospital.

____ ____ 2. Elsa wants to visit her at home.

____ ____ 3. Elsa sees a sign on the wall.

____ ____ 4. Visiting Hours are 10:00 A.M. to 7:30 P.M.

____ ____ 5. Elsa sees her friend at the reception desk.

____ ____ 6. She finds out her friend is in Room 579.

____ ____ 7. Elsa takes the elevator to the fifth floor.

____ ____ 8. The elevator is out of order.

____ ____ 9. There are many rooms on the fifth floor.

____ ____ 10. The nurse says, "Visiting Hours are over."

You decide.

Check the good things to bring to a friend in the hospital.

1. ____ flowers

2. ____ books

3. ____ cigars

4. ____ candy

5. ____ bathrobe

6. ____ pain medication

7. ____ get-well cards

8. ____ magazines

9. ____ pets

10. ____ cell phone

At the Reception Desk

Practice the dialog with a partner.

Hello. I'm here to visit my friend.
What's the name?
Her name is Erika Smith.
She is in Room 579.
Where is the elevator?
Turn left before the Exit sign.

Understanding Signs

Which sign can help Elsa? Write the word for the correct sign on each line.

Exit	Stairs	Out of Order	Reception

1. Elsa needs her friend's room number. _____

2. The elevator doesn't come. _____

3. Elsa goes up the steps to the fifth floor. _____

4. Elsa needs to go home. _____

Elsa's Visit

Listen to the events. Write the correct number next to each picture.

a. _____

d. _____

b. _____

e. _____

c. _____

f. _____

Complete the sentences.

1. Elsa's friend is in the _____.
   [elevator / hospital]

2. Elsa waits at the _____.
   [exit sign / reception desk]

3. Elsa takes the stairs to the _____ floor.
   [fifth / sixth]

4. The nurse says, "You can come back _____."
   [tomorrow / tonight]

Think about it.

What other signs can Elsa see at a hospital? Write your ideas on the lines.

_____   _____

_____   _____

Check *yes* or *no* about you.

Yes   No

____ ____   1. I visit people in the hospital.

____ ____   2. I know hospital visiting hours.

____ ____   3. I can read signs.

____ ____   4. I can understand signs.

LESSON 11

Talk about Smoking

Joe and his daughter are at home.
They are watching a movie on TV.
A beautiful actress is on the screen.
She lights a cigarette.

Joe looks at his daughter.
"Don't ever smoke," he says.
"Many people die from smoking.
They get **lung cancer** more than nonsmokers.
They get **heart disease** more than nonsmokers.
They are sick more than nonsmokers."

His daughter says, "Don't worry, Dad. I'm never smoking."

"Good," says Joe. "You don't want cancer."

"No!" says his daughter.

"Now please stop talking and watch the movie."

Complete the story.

Joe and his _____ are at home. They are watching
a movie on TV. A beautiful actress is on the screen. She lights a
_____ .

Joe looks at his daughter. "Don't ever _____ ," he
says. "Many people _____ from smoking. They get
lung _____ more than nonsmokers. They get heart
_____ more than nonsmokers. They are _____
more than nonsmokers."

His daughter says, "Don't worry, Dad. I'm _____
smoking." "Good," says Joe. "You don't want cancer."

"No!" says his daughter. "Now please stop talking and watch
the movie."

Check *yes* or *no*.

Yes   No

____ ____   1. Joe and his daughter are at the movie theater.

____ ____   2. They are at home.

____ ____   3. They are watching a movie on TV.

____ ____   4. A very sick woman is on the screen.

____ ____   5. The actress lights a cigarette.

____ ____   6. Joe says, "Don't ever smoke."

____ ____   7. Smokers get lung cancer more than nonsmokers.

____ ____   8. Smokers get heart disease more than nonsmokers.

____ ____   9. Nonsmokers are sick more than smokers.

____ ____   10. Joe's daughter wants to smoke.

You decide.

Check the body parts that smoking can hurt.

1. ____ heart

2. ____ lungs

3. ____ skin

4. ____ mouth

5. ____ eyes

6. ____ brain

7. ____ teeth

8. ____ fingernails

9. ____ gums

10. ____ throat

11. ____ muscles

12. ____ hair

Talking to the School Nurse

Practice the dialog with a partner.

I don't want my child to smoke.

Do you talk about it at home?

Yes, but it's difficult.

I know. Smoking is everywhere.

What can I say?

Tell her many people die from smoking.

Give her this to read.

Don't smoke!

Read the information from the school nurse. Then underline the correct answers.

- Every year, 440,000 Americans die from smoking.
- Smoking causes lung cancer and heart disease.
- Smokers get more infections than nonsmokers.
- Smokers have more colds, flu, bronchitis, and pneumonia than nonsmokers.

---

1. Every year (**44,000 / 440,000**) Americans die from smoking.

2. Smoking causes more lung cancer and heart (**disease / movies**).

3. Smokers get more (**infections / cigarettes**) than nonsmokers.

4. (**Smokers / People**) have more colds, flu, bronchitis, and pneumonia.

Watching a Movie

Listen. Write the correct number next to each picture.

a. ____

d. ____

b. ____

e. ____

c. ____

f. ____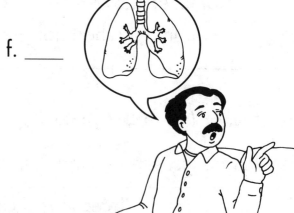

Complete the sentences.

1. Joe and his _____ are at home.
   [son / daughter]

2. Many people die from _____.
   [smoking / talking]

3. Smokers get more lung _____.
   [cancer / movies]

4. _____ are sick more than nonsmokers.
   [Actresses / Smokers]

Think about it.

What can Joe say about smoking? Write your ideas on the lines.

_____   _____

_____   _____

Check *yes* or *no* about you.

Yes   No

____ ____   1. I see people smoking in movies.

____ ____   2. I talk about smoking at home.

____ ____   3. I know about lung cancer.

____ ____   4. I know about heart disease.

LESSON 12

Flu Season

It's January.

It's **flu** season.

Many people are sick with the flu.

Hana and her family want to stay well.

Hana's father eats healthy food.

Hana's mother takes **vitamins.**

Her sister drinks orange juice.

Hana's grandmother gets a flu **shot.**

Her grandfather gets a lot of sleep.

Hana washes her hands often.

On Saturday, Hana visits her friend. She plays with her friend all day. She comes home with a terrible **headache.**

"Maybe I'm sick," says Hana. "Everyone in my friend's family has the flu."

Complete the story.

It's January. It's _____ season. Many people are sick with
₁

the flu. Hana and her _____ want to stay well.
₂

Hana's father eats _____ food. Hana's mother takes
₃

_____. Her sister drinks _____ juice. Hana's
₄   ₅

grandmother gets a flu _____. Her grandfather gets a lot
₆

of sleep. Hana washes her _____ often.
₇

On Saturday, Hana visits her friend. She plays with her

_____ all day. She comes home with a terrible
₈

_____. "Maybe I'm sick," says Hana. "Everyone in my
₉

friend's family has the flu."

Check *yes* or *no*.

Yes   No

____ ____   1. It's January.

____ ____   2. It's flu season.

____ ____   3. Hana and her family are sick with the flu.

____ ____   4. Hana's father eats healthy food.

____ ____   5. Hana's mother gets a flu shot.

____ ____   6. Hana washes her hands once a day.

____ ____   7. On Saturday, Hana visits her friend.

____ ____   8. She plays with her friend all day.

____ ____   9. Hana comes home with a terrible stomachache.

____ ____ 10. Her friend's family has the flu.

You decide.

Check the actions that can help you stay healthy.

1. ____ eat healthy food

2. ____ take vitamins

3. ____ get a flu shot

4. ____ visit sick friends

5. ____ wash your hands often

6. ____ take anti-viral medicine

7. ____ sleep

8. ____ touch your face

9. ____ take herbs

10. ____ drink orange juice

11. ____ stay home

12. ____ share drinks

Talking to the Doctor

Practice the dialog with a partner.

Do I need a flu shot?

How old are you?

I'm 67.

Yes. It's a good idea for people over 65.

When can I get it?

It's better to get it before flu season.

Flu Shot Notice

Read the flu shot notice. Then underline the correct answers.

Flu Shots

East River Public Health Center, 855 Field Street

Mondays, Tuesdays, Wednesdays, and Fridays: 8:00 A.M. to 11:00 A.M.

Thursdays: 1:00 P.M. to 4:00 P.M.

$10 fee   **Call for more information: 555-3840**

---

1. You can get a flu shot at the (**East / West**) River Public Health Center.

2. The address is (**885 / 855**) Field Street.

3. You can get a flu shot on (**Thursday / Friday**) from 1:00 P.M. to 4:00 P.M.

4. Flu shots cost (**$10 / $20**).

5. You can call for more information at (**555-8420 / 555-3840**).

Staying Well

Listen to the things Hana and her family are doing. Write the correct number next to each picture.

a. _____

d. _____

b. _____

e. _____

c. _____

f. _____

Complete the sentences.

1. Hana and her _____ want to stay well.
   [family / father]

2. Her _____ gets a flu shot.
   [grandfather / grandmother]

3. Hana washes her _____ often.
   [headache / hands]

4. She plays with her _____ all day.
   [flu / friend]

Think about it.

Hana has the flu. What can help her feel better? Write your ideas on the lines below.

_____   _____

_____   _____

Check *yes* or *no* about you.

Yes   No

____ ____   1. I eat healthy food.

____ ____   2. I take vitamins.

____ ____   3. I wash my hands often.

____ ____   4. I get a flu shot.

LESSON 13

Making an Appointment

George has a very **sore throat.**
He has some **fever** too.
He calls the doctor's office.
George hears a recording.
"Press *three* to make an **appointment,**" says a voice.
George presses *three.*

After a few minutes, a **receptionist** gets on the line.
George asks for an appointment.
The receptionist asks, "How about next week?"
"No," says George. "I'm sick now."
George gets an appointment for 4:30 P.M.

George **gargles** with warm salt water.
He drinks some tea with lemon.
His throat feels better.
He doesn't have a fever.
But he goes to the doctor anyway.
He doesn't want to get any sicker.

Complete the story.

George has a very sore _____. He has some fever too. He

₁

calls the doctor's office. George hears a _____. "Press three

₂

to make an _____," says a voice. George presses three.

₃

After a few _____, a receptionist gets on the line. George

₄

asks for an appointment. The receptionist asks, "How about next week?"

"No," says George. "I'm _____ now." George gets an

₅

appointment for 4:30 P.M.

George _____ with warm salt water. He drinks some

₆

_____ with lemon. His throat feels better. He doesn't have

₇

a fever. But he goes to the doctor anyway. He doesn't want to get any

_____.

₈

Check *yes* or *no*.

Yes   No

____ ____   1. George has a sore throat.

____ ____   2. He calls the doctor's office.

____ ____   3. George hears the doctor.

____ ____   4. George presses *two* to make an appointment.

____ ____   5. After a few seconds, a receptionist gets on the line.

____ ____   6. George asks for an appointment.

____ ____   7. George gets an appointment for 4:30 P.M.

____ ____   8. He gargles with tea with lemon.

____ ____   9. He drinks warm salt water.

____ ____   10. George goes to the doctor.

You decide.

Check the things that can help George feel better.

1. ____ salt water

2. ____ tea with lemon

3. ____ throat spray

4. ____ doctor

5. ____ cold water

6. ____ popsicles

7. ____ hard candy

8. ____ hot shower

9. ____ tea with honey

10. ____ pain medication

11. ____ cough drops

12. ____ toast

Talking to a Receptionist

Practice the dialog with a partner.

I want to make an appointment.

How about next week?

I'm sick now. I need to come
in today.

What's the problem?

I have a very sore throat.

The doctor can see you at 4:30 P.M.

An Appointment with the Doctor

Read George's note about his appointment. Underline the correct answers.

Doctor Amelia Chavez

Ph: 555-8496

4:30 P.M.

16755 Hillside Road / Suite 308

Remember $15 for co-payment

1. The doctor's last name is (**Lopez** / **Chavez**).

2. George's appointment is at (**3:30** / **4:30**) P.M.

3. The address is (**17655** / **16755**) Hillside Road.

4. George needs (**$15** / **$10**) for the co-payment.

George's Morning

Listen to the events. Write the correct number next to each picture.

a. _____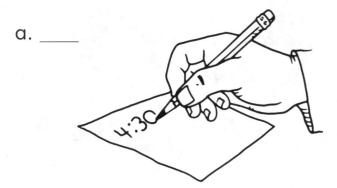

d. _____

b. _____

e. _____

c. _____

f. _____

Complete the sentences.

1. George has a sore _____.
   [thumb / throat]

2. He gets an appointment for _____.
   [4:30 P.M. / next week]

3. George drinks some _____ with lemon.
   [salt water / tea]

4. His throat feels better. But he _____ the doctor anyway.
   [makes / goes to]

Think about it.

What can help George feel better? Write your ideas on the lines.

_____   _____

_____   _____

Check *yes* or *no* about you.

Yes   No

____ ____   1. I can call the doctor's office.

____ ____   2. I gargle with salt water.

____ ____   3. I drink tea for a sore throat.

____ ____   4. I sometimes get a sore throat.

LESSON 14

A Burn in the Kitchen

Quon is a cook in a restaurant.
He is deep-frying egg rolls.
Hot oil splashes on his hand.
The oil **burns** his hand.
"Ouch!" says Quon.

Quon runs to the sink.
He holds his hand under cold water.
"Put ice on it," says the dishwasher.
"Put butter on it," says the waitress.
"No," says Quon.
"Those things are bad for a **burn.**"

Finally, Quon turns off the water.
He puts **ointment** on the burn.
He covers it with a **bandage.**
He goes back to the stove.
"I'm OK," says Quon.
"But these egg rolls look terrible."

Complete the story.

Quon is a _____ in a restaurant. He is deep-frying egg
                       1

rolls. Hot _____ splashes on his hand. The oil burns his
               2

hand. "Ouch!" says Quon.

Quon runs to the _____. He holds his hand under
                  3

_____ water. "Put ice on it," says the dishwasher. "Put butter
     4

on it," says the waitress.

"No," says Quon. "Those things are bad for a _____."
                                 5

Finally, Quon turns off the _____. He puts
                   6

_____ on the burn. He covers it with a _____.
     7   8

He goes back to the stove. "I'm OK," says Quon. "But these egg rolls

look terrible."

Check *yes* or *no*.

Yes   No

____ ____   1. Quon is a dishwasher in a restaurant.

____ ____   2. He is deep-frying egg rolls.

____ ____   3. Hot oil splashes on his hand.

____ ____   4. Quon runs to the hospital.

____ ____   5. He holds his hand under hot water.

____ ____   6. Quon puts ice on the burn.

____ ____   7. Finally, Quon turns off the water.

____ ____   8. He puts ointment on the burn.

____ ____   9. Quon covers the burn with butter.

____ ____   10. Quon is OK.

You decide.

Check the things you think Quon needs.

1. ____ ice

2. ____ cold water

3. ____ 911

4. ____ butter

5. ____ ointment

6. ____ hospital

7. ____ bandage

8. ____ paramedics

9. ____ cold compress

10. ____ aloe vera lotion

11. ____ powder

12. ____ pain medication

Talking to a Co-worker

Practice the dialog with a partner.

Ouch!

What happened?

I burned my hand!

Hold it under cold water.

Then what?

Put on some ointment and a bandage.

Ointment

Read the directions on the ointment. Then underline the correct answers.

Prevents infections. Helps the pain of minor burns.
For ages 2 and up.
Directions: Clean the affected area.
Put a small amount on the burn.
Use 1 to 3 times daily.
Cover with a sterile bandage.

1. This ointment helps the pain of (**minor / major**) burns.

2. It is for (**areas / ages**) 2 and up.

3. You can use this (**ointment / oil**) 1 to 3 times daily.

4. You can cover the burn with a sterile (**bandage / butter**).

Quon's Burn

Listen to the events. Write the correct number next to each picture.

a. _____

d. _____

b. _____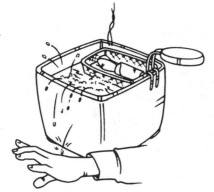

e. _____

c. _____

f. _____

Complete the sentences.

1. Quon splashes hot _____ on his hand.
   [oil / egg rolls]

2. Quon holds his hand _____ cold water.
   [over / under]

3. Finally Quon _____ the water.
   [turns on / turns off]

4. Quon is _____.
   [OK / terrible]

Think about it.

What can help Quon feel better? Write your ideas on the lines below.

_____   _____

_____   _____

Check *yes* or *no* about you.

Yes   No

____ ____   1. I cook with hot oil.

____ ____   2. I sometimes burn myself.

____ ____   3. I hold burns under cold water.

____ ____   4. I put other things on burns.

Health Words

Lesson 1: Too Much Sodium

blood – the red liquid in the body

blood pressure – the force of blood when it moves through the body

diet – the food that you eat

heart attack – a medical problem in which the heart stops working

mg – short form for milligram

milligram – a very small measure of weight

sodium – an element in salt

Lesson 2: Pollen Problems

allergy – a physical reaction from eating, breathing, or touching something that makes you sick

headache – a pain in the head

itchy – having a feeling that you need to rub your skin or a body part

over-the-counter – referring to medicine you can buy without a prescription or without going to a doctor

pollen – a powder from plants such as trees, flowers, or grass that makes other plants produce seeds

prescription – a piece of paper that a doctor writes that says what medicine a person needs; an order from a doctor for medicine

sneeze – to let air come out of the mouth and nose suddenly and with force

Lesson 3: Tired at Work

shoulder – the part of the body between the neck and the arm

tired – needing sleep or rest

Lesson 4: A Painting Accident

ambulance – a vehicle for taking people who are sick or injured to the hospital

balance – the ability to stay steady and not fall

bone – part of a skeleton; one of the hard parts in a person's body

broken – not whole; in two or more pieces

hurt – to cause pain or damage; to feel pain

x-ray – a photograph that can show the inside of the body, including broken bones

Lesson 5: More Exercise

energy – the power to be active

exercise – physical activity

overweight – too fat

Lesson 6: No More Candy

appointment – a specific day and time to see someone (such as a doctor)

cavity – a hole in a tooth

dentist – doctor for teeth

examine – look at closely

filling – material that is put into a cavity; dental process for putting material into a cavity

fluoride – a chemical in toothpaste or in water that helps protect teeth

x-ray – to take a photograph that shows the inside of a part of the body

Lesson 7: Wash Your Hands

wash – to clean with water and soap

wrist – the area between the hand and the arm

Lesson 8: Fever Medicine

dropper – a small plastic tube used for measuring liquids

expired – past the date when something is good to use; past the date on a label that tells how long a product is good to use

fever – a high body temperature

forehead – the part of the face above the eyes

medicine cabinet – a place in the bathroom for keeping medications and other items, usually above the sink

pharmacy – a store or an area in a store where you buy medications

temperature – the measure of how hot or cold the body is

virus – a very small living thing that causes a disease; also the disease that it causes

Lesson 9: Calling 911

chest – the front of the body below the neck and above the stomach

medication – another word for medicine; a drug; something you take if you are sick, to make you feel better

oxygen – a gas in the air that people and animals need in order to live

paramedic – a person who can help sick or injured people, but who is not a doctor or nurse; a paramedic often works on an ambulance

Lesson 10: Visiting Hours

hospital – a place to get medical help when you are sick or injured

nurse – a person who can take care of sick people

reception desk – the place near the entrance of a hospital where you can get information about patients, room numbers, etc.

Lesson 11: Talk about Smoking

cancer – a serious disease, in which certain cells in the body grow much faster than they should

disease – a sickness

heart – the organ that makes blood move through the body

lungs – the organ we use for breathing

Lesson 12: Flu Season

flu – an illness like a serious cold, caused by a virus; short form for influenza

headache – a pain in the head

shot – a way to get medication inside the body, using a special needle

vitamin – a chemical in food and in special pills that is important for keeping the body healthy

Lesson 13: Making an Appointment

appointment – a specific day and time to see someone (such as a doctor)

fever – a high body temperature

gargle – to move a liquid around in the throat, often to make the throat feel better

receptionist – the person in an office who makes appointments and greets people who come to the office

sore – painful; feeling that something hurts

throat – the part of the body at the back of the mouth; the inside of the neck

Lesson 14: A Burn in the Kitchen

bandage – a cloth or other material to put on a cut, burn, or other injury

burn – an injury from heat or fire; to cause that injury

ointment – medicine that you rub on your skin

Listening Exercise Prompts

Lesson 1
Understanding the Doctor (p. 8)
Write the correct number next to each picture.

1. High blood pressure can cause a heart attack.
2. Foods with a lot of sodium are not good for you.
3. Shop for fresh foods.
4. Read labels for sodium milligrams.
5. Don't put salt on your food.

Lesson 2
Understanding the Doctor (p. 14)
Write the correct number next to each picture.

1. Use an air conditioner.
2. Wear a mask outside.
3. Take allergy medicine.
4. Close the windows at home.
5. Stay inside when it's windy.
6. Use a dryer, not a clothesline.

Lesson 3
Check the correct picture. (p. 20)
1. Tina likes late-night TV.
2. Sometimes she watches TV until 1:30 a.m.
3. A co-worker taps her on the shoulder.
4. Tina puts her head down on the desk again.

Lesson 4
Doctor's Orders (p. 26)
Write the correct number next to each picture.

1. Look at your bone on the X-ray.
2. Take pain medication.
3. Wear a cast.
4. Use crutches for walking.
5. Get physical therapy.
6. Stay home. Don't work for six weeks.

Lesson 5
What Fran Does (p. 32)
Write the correct number next to each picture.

1. Fran goes to an exercise class.
2. She sits in the car.
3. She brings a bottle of water.
4. She sits at work.
5. She walks to the recreation center.
6. She sits at home.

Lesson 6
At the Dentist (p. 38)
Write the correct number next to each picture.

1. Gino eats a lot of candy.
2. Gino's teeth hurt.
3. The dentist examines Gino.
4. The dentist gives Gino a toothbrush.
5. Gino needs to brush twice a day.

Lesson 7
Wash your hands! (p. 44)
Write the correct number next to each picture.

1. Use soap and warm running water.
2. Rub your hands for 15 seconds.
3. Wash your wrists and the backs of your hands.
4. Wash between your fingers and under your fingernails.
5. Rinse well.
6. Dry your hands with a paper towel. Then turn off the water with a paper towel.

Lesson 8
Check the correct picture. (p. 50)
1. José doesn't feel well.
2. He has a fever.
3. Maria's forehead feels hot.
4. José takes child fever medicine.

Lesson 9
Emergency (p. 56)
Write the correct number next to each picture.

1. Dora is holding her chest.
2. Ming tells Dora not to worry.
3. Ming calls 911 on her cell phone.
4. The paramedics arrive in ten minutes.
5. They give her some oxygen.
6. Dora takes off the oxygen mask.

Lesson 10
Elsa's Visit (p. 62)
Write the correct number next to each picture.

1. Elsa sees a sign. Visiting Hours 10:00 A.M. to 8:30 P.M.
2. It is 8:00 p.m. now.
3. Elsa waits at the reception desk.
4. The elevator is out of order.
5. Elsa takes the stairs to the fifth floor.
6. The nurse says, "Sorry. Visiting Hours are over."

Lesson 11
Watching a Movie (p. 68)
Write the correct number next to each picture.

1. Joe and his daughter are watching a movie on TV.
2. A beautiful actress is on the screen.
3. The actress lights a cigarette.
4. Joe talks about lung cancer.
5. Joe talks about heart disease.
6. His daughter says, "Please stop talking!"

Lesson 12
Staying Well (p. 74)
Write the correct number next to each picture.

1. Hana's grandfather gets a lot of sleep.
2. Hana's mother takes vitamins.
3. Hana's sister drinks orange juice.
4. Hana's father eats healthy food.
5. Hana's grandmother gets a flu shot.
6. Hana washes her hands often.

Lesson 13
George's Morning (p. 80)
Write the correct number next to each picture.

1. George has a sore throat.
2. He presses three to make an appointment.
3. A receptionist gets on the line.
4. George gets an appointment for 4:30 p.m.
5. George gargles with warm salt water.
6. George drinks some tea with lemon.

Lesson 14
Quon's Burn (p. 86)
Write the correct number next to each picture.

1. Hot oil splashes on Quon's hand.
2. Quon runs to the sink.
3. Quon holds his hand under cold water.
4. The dishwasher says to put ice on it.
5. Quon puts ointment on the burn.
6. He covers it with a bandage.

Answer Key

Lesson 1
Complete the story. (p. 5)
1. high
2. heart
3. diet
4. label
5. sodium
6. eat
7. salt
8. lower

Check *yes* or *no*. (p. 6)
1. no
2. yes
3. yes
4. no
5. no
6. yes
7. no
8. yes
9. no
10. yes

Nutrition Facts (p. 7)
1. 890
2. cup
3. 215
4. low

Understanding the Doctor (p. 8)
a. 5
b. 3
c. 1
d. 4
e. 2

Complete the sentences. (p. 9)
1. high blood pressure
2. Sodium
3. Fresh foods
4. lower blood pressure

Lesson 2
Complete the story. (p. 11)
1. spring
2. pollen
3. allergy
4. windows
5. breathes
6. sneezes
7. headache
8. closes
9. Summer

Check *yes* or *no*. (p. 12)
1. no
2. yes
3. yes
4. no
5. yes
6. no
7. yes
8. no
9. no
10. yes

Allergies (p. 12)
1. perfume
2. medication
3. pets

Symptoms (p. 13)
Students should check 2 (watery eyes), 4 (sneezing), 8 (headache), and 9 (itchy eyes). They may also discuss other items as possible symptoms of allergies.

Understanding the Doctor (p. 14)
a. 3
b. 5
c. 2
d. 1
e. 6
f. 4

Complete the sentences. (p. 15)
1. spring
2. an allergy
3. itchy and watery
4. the windows

Lesson 3
Complete the story. (p. 17)
1. shows
2. watches
3. tired
4. co-worker
5. fired
6. sleep
7. head
8. favorite

Check *yes* or *no*. (p. 18)
1. yes
2. no
3. yes
4. no
5. no
6. yes
7. no
8. yes
9. yes
10. no

Employee Handbook (p. 19)
1. dismissed
2. sleeping on the job

Check the correct picture. (p. 20)
1. b
2. b
3. a
4. a

Complete the sentences. (p. 21)
1. late-night TV
2. falls asleep
3. shoulder
4. sleep

Lesson 4
Complete the story. (p. 23)
1. house
2. ladder
3. balance
4. leg
5. ambulance
6. x-ray
7. bone
8. paint

Check *yes* or *no*. (p. 24)
1. no
2. yes
3. yes
4. no
5. yes
6. no
7. yes
8. no
9. yes
10. no

Ladder Safety (p. 25)
Students should circle picture b.

Doctor's Orders (p. 26)
a. 6
b. 2
c. 5
d. 4
e. 1
f. 3

Complete the sentences. (p. 27)

1. house   3. an ambulance
2. balance   4. leg

Lesson 5

Complete the story. (p. 29)

1. exercise   5. blocks
2. energy   6. water
3. sit   7. car
4. class   8. tired

Check *yes* or *no*. (p. 30)

1. yes   5. no   8. no
2. no   6. no   9. no
3. yes   7. yes   10. yes
4. yes

Calories (p. 31)

1. 102   3. sitting at work
2. 264   4. walking

What Fran Does (p. 32)

a. 2   c. 6   e. 1
b. 3   d. 5   f. 4

Complete the sentences. (p. 33)

1. energy   3. home
2. class   4. tired

Lesson 6

Complete the story. (p. 35)

1. candy   5. cavities
2. brush   6. twice
3. teeth   7. fillings
4. dentist   8. toothbrush

Check *yes* or *no*. (p. 36)

1. no   5. no   8. yes
2. no   6. yes   9. no
3. yes   7. yes   10. yes
4. yes

Take care of your teeth. (p. 36)

1. toothpaste/toothbrush
2. dentist
3. x-ray

Toothpaste (p. 37)

1. fluoride   3. after
2. cavities   4. twice

At the Dentist (p. 38)

a. 3   c. 2   e. 4
b. 5   d. 1

Complete the sentences. (p. 39)

1. candy   3. teeth
2. brush   4. toothbrush

Lesson 7

Complete the story. (p. 41)

1. restaurant   5. restroom
2. hands   6. wash
3. food   7. help
4. floor   8. dirty

Check *yes* or *no*. (p. 42)

1. yes   5. no   8. yes
2. yes   6. no   9. yes
3. no   7. no   10. no
4. yes

Wash your hands! (p. 44)

a. 3   c. 5   e. 2
b. 1   d. 6   f. 4

Complete the sentences. (p. 45)

1. worker   3. seconds
2. washes   4. towel

Lesson 8

Complete the story. (p. 47)

1. son   5. date
2. temperature   6. expired
3. fever   7. pharmacy
4. medicine   8. adult

Check *yes* or *no*. (p. 48)

1. no   5. no   8. yes
2. yes   6. yes   9. no
3. yes   7. yes   10. yes
4. no

Taking Medicine (p. 49)

1. 1.6 mL   3. April 2008
2. two times   4. 6:00

Check the correct picture. (p. 50)

1. b.   3. a.
2. a   4. a

Complete the sentences. (p. 50)

1. child   3. adult   5. child
2. adult   4. adult   6. adult

Complete the sentences. (p. 51)

1. degrees
2. medicine cabinet
3. date
4. expired

Lesson 9

Complete the story. (p. 53)

1. neighbors
2. chest
3. worry
4. pains
5. paramedics
6. oxygen
7. old
8. mask

Check *yes* or *no*. (p. 54)

1. no
2. yes
3. yes
4. no
5. yes
6. no
7. no
8. yes
9. yes
10. yes

Dora's Purse (p. 55)

Compare picture to numbered words.

Emergency (p. 56)

a. 3
b. 6
c. 2
d. 4
e. 1
f. 5

Complete the sentences. (p. 57)

1. chest
2. well
3. 911
4. oxygen

Lesson 10

Complete the story. (p. 59)

1. hospital
2. sign
3. Hours
4. reception
5. waits
6. Out
7. stairs
8. nurse

Check *yes* or *no*. (p. 60)

1. yes
2. no
3. yes
4. no
5. no
6. yes
7. no
8. yes
9. yes
10. yes

Understanding Signs (p. 61)

1. Reception
2. Out of order
3. Stairs
4. Exit

Elsa's Visit (p. 62)

a. 3
b. 4
c. 6
d. 5
e. 1
f. 2

Complete the sentences. (p. 63)

1. hospital
2. reception desk
3. fifth
4. tomorrow

Lesson 11

Complete the story. (p. 65)

1. daughter
2. cigarette
3. smoke
4. die
5. cancer
6. disease
7. sick
8. never

Check *yes* or *no*. (p. 66)

1. no
2. yes
3. yes
4. no
5. yes
6. yes
7. yes
8. yes
9. no
10. no

Don't smoke! (p. 67)

1. 440,000
2. disease
3. infections
4. Smokers

Watching a Movie (p. 68)

a. 2
b. 5
c. 1
d. 6
e. 3
f. 4

Complete the sentences. (p. 69)

1. daughter
2. smoking
3. cancer
4. Smokers

Lesson 12

Complete the story. (p. 71)

1. flu
2. family
3. healthy
4. vitamins
5. orange
6. shot
7. hands
8. friend
9. headache

Check *yes* or *no*. (p. 72)

1. yes
2. yes
3. no
4. yes
5. no
6. no
7. yes
8. yes
9. no
10. yes

Flu Shot Notice (p. 73)

1. East
2. 855
3. Thursday
4. $10
5. 555-3840

Staying Well (p. 74)

a. 5
b. 6
c. 1
d. 4
e. 3
f. 2

Complete the sentences. (p. 75)

1. family
2. grandmother
3. hands
4. friend

Lesson 13

Complete the story. (p. 77)

1. throat
2. recording
3. appointment
4. minutes
5. sick
6. gargles
7. tea
8. sicker

Check *yes* or *no*. (p. 78)

1. yes
2. yes
3. no
4. no
5. no
6. yes
7. yes
8. no
9. no
10. yes

An Appointment with the Doctor (p. 79)

1. Chavez
2. 4:30
3. 16755
4. $15

George's Morning (p. 80)

a. 4
b. 5
c. 3
d. 6
e. 1
f. 2

Complete the sentences. (p. 81)

1. throat
2. 4:30 p.m.
3. tea
4. goes to

Lesson 14

Complete the story. (p. 83)

1. cook
2. oil
3. sink
4. cold
5. burn
6. water
7. ointment
8. bandage

Check *yes* or *no*. (p. 84)

1. no
2. yes
3. yes
4. no
5. no
6. no
7. yes
8. yes
9. no
10. yes

Ointment (p. 85)

1. minor
2. ages
3. ointment
4. bandage

Quon's Burn (p. 86)

a. 3
b. 1
c. 5
d. 2
e. 6
f. 4

Complete the sentences. (p. 87)

1. oil
2. under
3. turns off
4. OK